Contents

Introduction

Charitable and voluntary organisations enjoy tremendous support throughout the country. Many people are happy to spare their time and enthusiasm to get involved in different and often exciting activities to help others. Taking part in charitable work or voluntary schemes offers a lot of enjoyment and fun for those involved. But it is important to make sure that whatever activities are arranged, they are done so safely and in a way that will not pose any harm to health.

This guidance is designed to help you, as a charity or as an organisation that uses voluntary workers, to understand your health and safety responsibilities. The guidance covers these responsibilities towards your employees, and also to your voluntary workers. It offers advice on health and safety law, and on the type of preventive and protective measures that you might need to take for ensuring your workers' health and safety. In this booklet, the term 'workers' includes employees and those working voluntarily for an employer.

Charitable and voluntary work involves a wide range of work activities, each with their own particular risk. For instance, it can range from working in a charity shop, collecting donations outside a station and delivering meals-on-wheels, to more hazardous activities such as working on construction schemes using power tools.

It isn't possible to deal with all the risks from a wide range of work activities in a single booklet. So while this guidance is not comprehensive, it offers a guide to some of the main things you may need to do to comply with your legal duties, and ensure the health and safety of your workers.

Where voluntary work involves particular risks, eg violence to staff, there is likely to be specific guidance on how to deal with those risks (further information is given in the list of useful HSE publications towards the end of this booklet).

Legal duties

Health and safety law

The main piece of health and safety legislation is the Health and Safety at Work etc Act 1974 (the HSW Act). This sets out the general duties which employers, the self-employed, and people in control of premises have towards their employees, and others who could be affected by the work activities. It also gives employees the general duty to ensure the health and safety of themselves and each other.

There are also several sets of regulations made under the HSW Act which make these general duties more explicit. Some of these regulations apply across the full range of workplaces and work activities, while others apply to more specific situations. Details of some of these legal requirements are described later in this guidance. A list of the most significant regulations can be found on page 63.

General duties of employers and the self-employed

Where any organisation, such as a charity, has at least one paid employee anywhere in their organisation, it is considered to be an 'employer' for the purposes of the HSW Act and the regulations made under it.

Section 2 of the HSW Act places a duty on employers to ensure, so far as is reasonably practicable, the health, safety and welfare of their employees while at work.

Section 3 of the HSW Act places a duty on employers and the self-employed to conduct their undertakings in a way that ensures, so far as is reasonably practicable, that people other than their employees (eg voluntary workers, clients, customers and members of the public) are not exposed to risks to their health or safety.

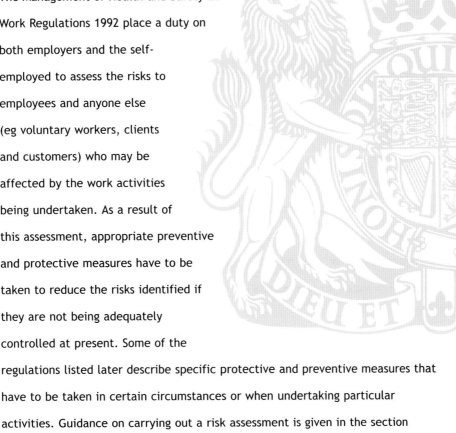

The Management of Health and Safety at
Work Regulations 1992 place a duty on
both employers and the self-
employed to assess the risks to
employees and anyone else
(eg voluntary workers, clients
and customers) who may be
affected by the work activities
being undertaken. As a result of
this assessment, appropriate preventive
and protective measures have to be
taken to reduce the risks identified if
they are not being adequately
controlled at present. Some of the
regulations listed later describe specific protective and preventive measures that
have to be taken in certain circumstances or when undertaking particular
activities. Guidance on carrying out a risk assessment is given in the section
'Risk assessment'.

Other general duties in health and safety law

Section 4 of the HSW Act places a duty on people in control of non-domestic
premises (eg a landlord, or the employer or person in charge of a shop) to ensure,
so far as is reasonably practicable, that access arrangements and any equipment
or substance in the premises are safe and without risk to health. The duty is in
relation to non-employees, (eg voluntary workers) who use the premises as a
place of work, or where they may use equipment or substances provided for their
use there.

There are also more specific duties in relation to a workplace in the Workplace (Health, Safety and Welfare) Regulations 1992. Some of these apply to employers and also to those who have, to any extent, control of a workplace.

Application of health and safety standards to voluntary workers

In general, the same health and safety standards should be applied to voluntary workers as they would to employees exposed to the same risks. However, if the risk assessment shows that the risks to voluntary workers are different, the preventive and protective measures taken should reflect the different risks.

HSE considers it good practice for a volunteer user to provide the same level of health and safety protection as they would in an employer/employee relationship, irrespective of whether there are strict legal duties.

Where can I go for advice?

Health and safety law is enforced by inspectors from HSE or by environmental health officers from your local authority. Local authorities have responsibility for inspecting most charity premises, activities and events, and can be approached for advice or guidance on health and safety at work.

In addition, the section 'Reporting accidents and work-related ill health' contains more information on the requirements under the Reporting of Injuries, Diseases and Dangerous Occurrences Regulations 1995 (RIDDOR).

If you have any doubts about your health and safety responsibilities towards your employees or others who may be affected by your work activities or your undertaking, you should seek further advice.

Risk assessment

Employers and the self-employed have a legal duty under the Management of Health and Safety at Work Regulations 1992, to assess the risks to the health and safety of their employees and others, including voluntary workers. This risk assessment is nothing more than a careful examination of what, in your work, could cause harm to people. It then helps you to decide whether you have taken enough precautions or should do more to prevent harm (remember, 'risk' is the chance, big or small, of harm actually being done).

Assessing the risks

HSE recommends a *5 step* approach to risk assessment.

Step 1   Look for the hazards.

'Hazard' means anything that can cause harm (eg chemicals and other hazardous substances, electricity, working from ladders). Look at all your work activities, including non-routine tasks. Look at what **actually** happens rather than what **should** happen.

Step 2   Decide who might be harmed, and how.

For example there are employees, voluntary workers, members of the public. Think about how people may be at risk - does their work involve manual handling, visiting people in their home, working with the public?

Step 3   For each hazard, evaluate the chance, big or small, of harm actually being done and decide whether existing precautions are adequate or more should be done.

For example, for each hazard, consider what would be the worst result? Would it be a broken finger or someone being killed? How likely is it to happen?

If you consider more needs to be done to control the risk, ask yourself if you can avoid the hazard by doing the job in a different way. If not, you need to think about controlling the hazard more effectively. For example:

- choose the most important things to tackle first;

- work with your employees and voluntary workers to solve problems and agree precautions;

- don't forget that new training and information could be needed.

Remember, even after all precautions have been taken, some risk will often remain. The important things you need to decide are whether the hazard is significant, and whether you have controlled it by satisfactory precautions so that the risk is as small as possible. You need to check this when you assess the risks.

Step 4   Record the significant findings of your risk assessment, eg the main risks and the measures you have taken to deal with them.

A 'significant' hazard has the potential to cause serious harm. You can keep paper or electronic records; it's up to you, but make sure your records are easily accessible. Remember, you only need to record your significant findings. These would include the hazards, existing control measures, and the people who may be affected.

Step 5   Review your assessment from time to time, and revise if necessary.

Remember that things change; you might take on new work. Rules get broken and people don't always do as they've been told. The only way to find out about changes like these is by checking. Don't wait until things have gone wrong. Check that the hazards are the same and that the precautions are adequate.

You can do the risk assessment yourself. If you work in a larger organisation, you could ask a safety officer, safety representative or responsible employee to help you. If you are not confident, your local environmental health officer or local HSE inspector can advise you. But remember - you are responsible for seeing that the risk assessment is done and is adequate.

Information, instruction and training

Health and safety law requires you to provide information, instruction and training for your employees. HSE considers it good practice for a volunteer user to provide the same level of health and safety information, instruction and training as they would in an employer/employee relationship. To help you in your approach to health and safety, this section sets out, in five easy steps, what you need to do.

Information

Information means providing factual material to people about risks and health and safety measures.

Step 1   Decide **who** needs information.

This would include your employees, your voluntary workers, temporary staff, people visiting your premises, etc.

Step 2   Decide **what** information needs to be covered.

This would include health and safety risks, precautions for preventing these risks or protecting against them, how to use work equipment, how to work with members of the public (eg how to diffuse conflict or aggression).

Step 3   Decide **when** information is needed.

Usually, the answer is: in enough time for it to be acted on. So think about what your employees and voluntary workers need when they start work or perform a job for the first time.

Step 4   Decide **how** you are going to provide the information.

Think about the amount of information, who needs it and when. You can provide it :

- by telling people what they need to know;

- in written form;

- by letting people use information held on computer.

Make sure the information is easy to understand. Make sure that the people receiving it know why they are getting it and what they're expected to do with it.

Step 5   **Check** that the information has been effective.

Has everyone understood?

Has the information been correctly acted on?

Instruction and training

Instruction means telling people what they should and should not do. Training means helping them learn how to do it.

Step 1   Decide **who** needs to be trained.

Remember to think about managers and supervisors too, particularly if there is work equipment involved or the work is being done off-site.

Step 2   Decide **what** training is needed and what the objectives are.

Giving people the wrong training or too much is a waste of time and money.

Does the law require you to carry out specific training?

You can use your organisation's experience to help you decide what is needed.

Step 3   Decide **how** to carry out training.

You might already have a training programme for your employees but your voluntary workers need to be trained too. Learning from an experienced person on the job is a time-honoured form of training and probably the one used most with voluntary workers. But its value depends on how good the 'trainer' is.

If you use this method, it might be useful to consider giving the trainers some training too!

Step 4   Decide **when** to provide training.

Usually the answer is: before the person takes up the job or undertakes the task.

Step 5   **Check** that the training has worked.

Fund-raising

This section looks at a common activity of the charity and voluntary sector: fund-raising. Fund-raising ranges from small local fairs and fetes, to sponsored activities such as bungee jumps, all the way up to nationally supported annual events. A number of agencies, including local environmental health departments and insurance companies, can advise you on the management of risks at larger events, but the smaller fund-raising events must not be forgotten.

What do I need to think about?

This largely depends on the type of fund-raising event that you have in mind. The *5 step* approach to risk assessment offers the best way to approach an event, particularly one that is new or unfamiliar, as it will help you highlight the areas that you need to think about.

You need to consider how the event is planned and managed. Decisions about the suitability of the event, an appropriate site, the number of people needed to help with the event and the management of the likely activities are all important at the planning stage.

It might be useful at this stage to consider an example and apply some of this guidance to an actual event. Let's look at the types of health and safety issues that might need to be considered at a local fete.

Case study: local fete

You may find it useful to think about the fete as a whole. Concentrate on the significant hazards which could result in serious harm or affect several people.

For example, you may want to look carefully at issues ranging from communication, first aid and parking to the use of marquees, trestle tables and even bouncy castles. The following paragraphs provide examples of the issues to consider.

Communication

Good health and safety practice involves good communication about risks and precautions. You may find it helpful to appoint someone, or a group of people, to be in charge of the arrangements for the event and its planning. They can consider the hazards, risks and precautions of the event as a whole and also the different attractions and activities on offer.

If you choose a group to oversee the event, you could invite representatives of the stall holders and those running the attractions on to the group. The group's discussions will help to ensure that any problems that do arise can be resolved quickly. You may want to think about using mobile telephones or pagers to ensure that the organisers can communicate easily with others, particularly first-aid stations and some of the attractions.

You may find it helpful to approach other charities or organisations that have held similar events to learn from their experiences.

First aid

The Health and Safety (First Aid) Regulations 1981 require employers to provide first-aid facilities for their employees. Although there is no requirement for the organisers of an event such as a fete to provide first aid for people they do not employ, you may want to consider providing first aid for the public. The types of injuries or illnesses likely to occur at a fete are heart attacks, sunstroke (on a hot summer day), and minor injuries such as cuts and bruises. You may want to ask if any of your employees or voluntary workers involved in the event are qualified first aiders. If not, your local ambulance service or voluntary first-aid organisations, such as the St John Ambulance, can advise you and may be able to provide cover or assistance.

Spacing between stands and attractions

Plan the layout of the fete. If you have a coconut shy or a hoopla stall, is there enough room for people to throw the balls and hoops safely?

Use of temporary trestle tables

Are they appropriate for hot tea/coffee stands? The tables could be standing on uneven ground and may be knocked by crowds attending the fete.

Car/vehicle parking

If you intend to provide a car park, you may need designated marshals to guide the cars. Parking marshals need to wear a fluorescent vest so that they can be easily seen. Vehicles need to be routed away from pedestrians where possible.

Stall holders/keepers

Storage may present problems. Are there heavy items? How will you arrange for these to be lifted or moved safely? Do the stall holders understand what they need to do? Are there any specific instructions needed?

Cash handling

You need to think carefully about how the cash raised from the different stalls and attractions will be managed. You may want to arrange a safe system for a cash 'pick-up' at regular intervals rather than leaving open cash boxes in public view.

Cables and wiring for lighting and the PA system

Make sure that electrical cables are laid away from public thoroughfares, and that equipment is properly installed and a competent person has inspected it.

Use of marquees

Marquees should be erected by competent people with all the supporting poles, frames, guys, stakes, anchors, fastenings, etc, checked regularly on site. Marquees and large tents should be capable of withstanding bad weather conditions such as strong winds and heavy rain. Exit routes from marquees may be located over uneven ground, temporary flooring, duckboards, ramps, etc. These should be taken into account to ensure that there are safe entry and exit routes.

Use of a bouncy castle (or similar attraction)

You should arrange for one or more competent people to supervise the attraction at all times. You may need to put up signs indicating any age or height restrictions that may apply to the equipment - the suppliers of the equipment can advise on this.

Other special attractions

You need to consider any specific health and safety requirements if you have special attractions, such as a tractor ride or farmyard animals.

Fireworks

HSE has published specific guidance on firework displays. Details are given at the end of this booklet.

Insurance

Employer and public liability insurance cover (a minimum public indemnity of £1 000 000) may be needed.

Accidents

If an accident does occur, you may need to report it to the relevant authority. More detail on the types of accident that should be reported is provided in the section 'Reporting accidents and work-related ill health'.

Food hygiene and mobile vendors

You need to store and serve food properly. Some foods need to be kept refrigerated or stored separately from other food types. Serving utensils and appropriate hygiene clothing should also be used, eg plastic gloves, aprons and hats. Are the toilet and washing facilities located away from food stalls? Your local environmental health department can advise on food hygiene requirements.

Waste

Finally, don't forget to dispose of any waste and rubbish safely.

Evaluation

Afterwards, you need to evaluate the success of the event and take forward any lessons you have learnt.

- Who attended the event, for example a high proportion of elderly people?

- Which procedures worked, which didn't and why?

- If you received advice from the authorities, eg local authorities, HSE, local police and fire service - was it useful? Did it cover all your concerns?

- Were there any accidents or near misses? What happened, how were they managed?

Local environmental health officers, police, fire service or HSE inspectors (for fairground equipment other than a bouncy castle) can help with specific questions or more general guidance.

Remember, if you plan and manage the event properly, everyone will enjoy and benefit from a safe, successful day.

Charity shops

Charity shops and outlets are responsible for raising much of the funding used by charitable and voluntary organisations. The Workplace (Health, Safety and Welfare) Regulations 1992 apply to all workplaces and cover a wide range of basic health, safety and welfare issues such as ventilation, heating, lighting, workstations, seating and welfare facilities. Not all of the requirements of the Workplace Regulations apply if no employees work at the premises. But you still need to assess the risks to any voluntary workers who work there.

As well as addressing the issues described above, you may also need to look carefully at the issues described in the following paragraphs.

Clutter in the shop, such as stored clothes and books and high-level storage of goods

Materials and objects should be stored and stacked in such a way that they are not likely to fall and cause injury. Racking should be of adequate strength and stability having regard to the loads placed on it and its vulnerability to damage.

Use of stepladders (particularly by elderly voluntary workers)

Think about the safest way to store items. Can the use of a stepladder be avoided?

Old equipment or equipment in poor repair

Workplace equipment should be maintained in effective working order and in good repair so that it does not present a risk to anyone, eg irons, ironing boards and

washing machines used to prepare donated clothes for resale. You need to ensure that any equipment provided for use at work, including machinery, is safe and that your workers know how to operate it safely.

Safety of second-hand and donated electrical appliances, and other goods for intended use or resale

The local trading standards department of your local authority will be happy to provide free advice and also has a variety of leaflets and literature you may find useful.

Delivery of unknown goods to the shop

You need to think about manual handling risks, and possible exposure to hazardous substances.

Cash handling

Bank money more frequently and vary the route taken to reduce the risk of robbery.

Security and work-related violence

There is always a risk of theft, and assault or abuse of workers by customers.

If you have retail outlets as part of your fund-raising activities, you may want to think about talking to organisations such as the British Retail Consortium about the sorts of preventative measures that you could take. These might include: installing higher counters; the placing of cash tills; the importance of clear windows so that an aggressor is clearly visible.

You may also want to think about linking up with other retail outlets in terms of identifying potentially violent people. The location of the shop is important, and you need to consider whether more than one person needs to be present.

Working off-site

There are a number of jobs that require both employees and voluntary workers to work away from their employer's base. This may involve working at isolated premises, in clients' homes, at another employer's premises, or travelling between sites (which carries with it other hazards). While many of the hazards faced by people working off-site are no different from those in any workplace, the risk arising from them can be greater since there is little or no direct supervision of the work activity. The aim of this section is to help you consider the health and safety implications for working off-site.

What do I need to think about?

Because of the many different activities undertaken by charitable and voluntary organisations, their workers are often called upon to carry out all sorts of work off-site. This could range from visiting elderly people in their own homes, taking children or people with disabilities on adventure holidays, to helping with environmental issues. It is not possible to cover all these activities, but this section offers some suggestions to help you get started. For example, you might want to look carefully at the following areas.

Communication

A suitable off-site working system would involve effective communication with the work base (or an agreed central point). This would include a way of reporting back, perhaps at an agreed time or at regular periods, to ensure that contact is maintained. You should consider how those working off-site can contact base or others, particularly in an emergency or if first aid is needed.

Information, instruction and training

Workers need to have enough information to make decisions about what is safe for them to do and about the methods they can use. They may have to refuse a service to a client if the service cannot be provided safely, for example withdrawing a care service where a dependent client refuses to allow the use of a hoist. Do your employees and voluntary workers have sufficient information about the type of work you have asked them to do? Think about any special areas that may need particular training or instruction.

First aid

You are responsible for meeting the first-aid needs of your employees working away from the main base. You may need to make special arrangements for employees or voluntary workers who work alone or in remote areas. You may also need to consider whether travelling workers need to carry a personal first-aid kit.

Personal safety

This is an important issue, particularly for those workers who carry out home visits or have to work alone. Do you ensure that your workers plan their journeys or visits beforehand? Ask if the route is familiar to them. Is the site isolated? Is it in a poorly lit or maintained area? What method of transport is being used - private car or public transport? Is the station close to the work site? Does the public transport run late at night or at times to suit shift work?

You may also want to think about specific issues such as identifying clients'

relatives, friends and even pets who might present a risk, and who are likely to

be present at a home visit to a client.

It is wise to always ensure that a designated person at the work base is aware

that a staff member or voluntary worker is working off-site, knows the details of

their visits, and when they are expected back.

Outdoor working

You may want to think about what facilities are available for meals, toilets,

extreme weather conditions, etc.

Remember to look at previous examples or 'near misses' that may help to identify

possible hazards. You could also contact other organisations who are operating

similar processes to see how they approach potential problems and identify

practical solutions.

What about working at other employers' premises

When your employees are working at another employer's premises, that second employer also has legal duties under health and safety law. The law requires co-operation and co-ordination between yourself and that employer. The main purpose of this is to ensure that everybody involved is aware of the risks in the workplace, and that all necessary steps are taken to reduce those risks. This is particularly important if the second employer is providing any equipment to help you carry out your work: they need to know exactly what the task involves and how it is going to be done, so that any equipment they provide is suitable.

Your employees, and any other person working in your undertaking, must be informed about any risks to their health and safety that are associated with the second employer's work activities and premises, and about relevant arrangements at the premises. The arrangements include the action that employees and others have to take to comply with emergency procedures set down by the second employer, eg reporting accidents, fire alarms and evacuations and first aid.

The second employer, or person in charge of the other premises, also has a right to information on any risks to their employees' health and safety out of or in connection with your work activities.

Working with equipment

We all use a wide range of equipment to help us do our work. Work equipment includes virtually anything that your workers have to use in their job, such as personal computers, electrical appliances, hoists, ladders, and powered and non-powered tools.

New equipment is covered by several pieces of legislation which place duties for safe design and minimum levels of protection on designers, manufacturers and suppliers. Suppliers of second-hand equipment must also make sure that the equipment they supply is safe and without risk to health.

Charity and voluntary workers, in common with other workers, use a variety of work equipment from a number of different sources, eg new, second-hand, or from donations.

You need to ensure that equipment used by your employees and voluntary workers does not give rise to risks to health and safety, irrespective of its age or place of origin. You may also have to consider the use of electricity on work premises and at outdoor events, eg for energy supply and lighting.

The aim of this section is to help raise your awareness of the need to ensure that:

● work equipment is correctly maintained; and

● workers are fully trained in its use in accordance with manufacturer/supplier instructions.

What do I need to think about?

You need to decide priorities and allocate resources, after considering the likelihood of injury or ill health occurring, its severity, and the people likely to be exposed to the hazard. A manufacturer's guidance may not cover all tasks, eg using ladders in a reception area with high ceilings. Systems of safe storage and isolation of equipment must be in place.

What do employees and others need to know?

People using the equipment need to have sufficient training or experience, qualifications, knowledge and skill to use the equipment safely. You need to think about providing workers and their supervisors with information, instructions or (where necessary) training on the safe use of equipment.

Employees have a duty to follow instructions and use work equipment properly. The information workers receive needs to cover:

- any risks to their health and safety;

- the procedures or safe systems of work including 'permit to work' systems that they must follow; and

- the personal protective equipment that is to be used.

Personal protective equipment is only an option where there are no other practical alternatives.

Employees and voluntary workers also need to know how to report defective or damaged equipment and to whom, where to obtain replacements and what maintenance is necessary. This information needs to be easy to understand. You may need to think more carefully if some of your employees or voluntary workers cannot easily understand English or if they have impaired literacy.

Special consideration should be given to the training needs of young people under 18 years of age.

Donated equipment

Charities and voluntary organisations are often donated new and second-hand work equipment for use both in their workplaces or for fund-raising purposes. If you choose to accept such equipment for use at work, you have a duty to ensure that it is safe and meets legal requirements before the equipment is used.

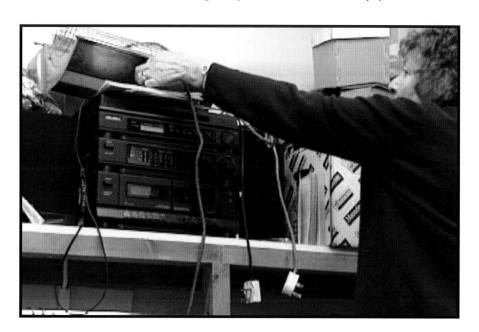

If you use tools that you have hired or leased, the person who provides them has the main duty to ensure that they are safe. You could, however, make enquiries about such things as whether any lifting equipment has been tested or what steps have been taken to ensure the safety of electrical equipment.

You need to seek advice from your local trading standards department regards the supply of all consumer goods (in particular electrical items and toys). The section 'Charity shops' has some additional information.

Electrical equipment

Working on electrical equipment

Anyone carrying out work on electrical equipment, eg safety inspection, testing or repairs, should be competent to do the work. That is, they should have the necessary knowledge and experience to do the work without risk to themselves or others.

Selection of electrical equipment

When selecting electrical equipment, you should ensure it is suitable for its intended purpose and for the conditions it will be used in. In particular, if equipment will be used in wet conditions, it should be designed for these.

Portable electrical equipment

The use of multi adapters should be avoided if insufficient socket outlets are available. Properly designed and fused extension blocks should be used. Additional trailing wires need to be controlled and protected from damage.

Portable residual current devices (RCDs) can help to prevent shocks, burns and fatalities from mains voltage equipment by isolating the power. RCDs are inexpensive and provide additional protection for outdoor electrical equipment. For instance, they can be used for lawnmowers and for equipment in premises such as community halls and pubs where the condition of the electrical systems (and loaned equipment) is not known or easily assessed. If a piece of equipment regularly makes an RCD trip out, have the equipment checked for faults by a competent person. RCDs can develop faults themselves. They are provided with a test button which should be used regularly. If the RCD fails to trip out when the test button is pressed, it should be removed from service and inspected or tested by a competent person. Include RCDs in your equipment maintenance system.

Fuses

Fuses prevent overloading of the appliance and are rated according to the power requirements. New domestic electrical equipment should be supplied with an integral plug, fitted with an appropriately rated fuse. When replacing fuses, follow the manufacturer's instructions on correct fuse ratings. In older equipment, you must take measures to ensure that wrongly rated fuses are never fitted to equipment or systems.

Maintaining electrical equipment

Portable electrical equipment should be maintained to prevent danger. A visual inspection of the equipment, cable, plug and socket before use will identify any obvious damage. Markings on equipment must be clearly visible. Many organisations have introduced a 'portable appliance testing' system as part of their maintenance programme. Hazards associated with portable equipment include trailing wires and overloaded sockets.

HSE publishes free guidance on maintaining portable electrical equipment in low-risk environments; details can be found in the list of useful HSE publications at the end of this booklet.

Maintaining electrical installations

In premises where you are responsible for the safety of fixed electrical wiring, you should also make sure this is maintained. The Institution of Electrical Engineers (IEE) produce standards for building wiring systems and publish BS 7671:1992 *Requirements for electrical installations*, the industry standard which is recognised and accepted as good practice. The standard recommends that wiring systems are inspected and tested at regular intervals by competent people with the appropriate experience, qualifications, knowledge and skills.

Display screen equipment (DSE)

The use of display screen equipment (DSE) is covered in the section 'Musculoskeletal disorders'.

What should my risk assessment cover?

This very much depends on the equipment you are using. But if you work your way through the *5 step* process, you should identify all the main hazards and how to control them. To get you started though, these are some of the hazards that can arise when using machinery and equipment:

- equipment catching fire or overheating, eg irons or heaters;

- explosions;

- electrical hazards, eg shock or burns;

- ejected objects such as stones from lawnmower blades;

- rupture or disintegration of equipment, eg water-heating boilers;

- unintended or premature discharge, eg electric stapling guns or steam from steamers.

You need to ensure that the equipment and its attachments, eg plugs and cables, are suitable for the job and for the environment in which they will be used, for instance indoor or outdoor. You also need to determine whether they have been maintained and repaired in accordance with manufacturer/supplier instructions. Wherever the equipment is being used, there must be sufficient light, either natural or artificial, and it should be in a stable position, eg on a suitable workbench. It may be useful to introduce a programme of planned preventative maintenance (PPM) for all work equipment so that defects or faults are detected and corrected at an early stage.

What control measures are needed?

This depends on what hazards you have identified. You will probably be using guidance from suppliers and distributors to help you ensure that adequate precautions are in place, but it may not exist for some tasks, for example using a lawnmower on a slope.

The main factors to take into account when deciding on appropriate precautions are the likelihood of injury or ill health occurring, its possible severity, and the people likely to be exposed to the hazard. Where the risk and potential severity is high, consideration must be given to suspending the work and finding safer alternative means.

Systems of safe storage and isolation of equipment must be in place. This is especially important in organisations where the young and vulnerable have access to the premises.

It is useful to speak to others who have experience to help you. Workers using the equipment may have previous experience of the measures needed to work safely, and can help you with the risk assessment. Where a comprehensive inspection of a piece of equipment is necessary, a competent qualified person may be required, eg for lifts. Where external contractors are employed for this purpose, you have a legal duty to ensure that the contractor has sufficient training, experience and knowledge to undertake the task.

You may also find it useful to keep details of the following:

- planned preventative maintenance/repair log books;

- training information including names of individuals trained and course content;

- documented safe working procedures, eg permits to work;

- personal protective equipment procedure log (if needed).

Where can I go for advice?

Information is generally available from suppliers and distributors. Your local environmental health officers or the local HSE office can advise on specific health and safety issues relating to work equipment. Your local trading standards officers can advise you on the sale of second-hand or donated equipment, particularly the safety of electrical appliances. You may also choose to approach relevant trade organisations. Guidance about specific pieces of equipment can be obtained from HSE inspectors and environmental health officers, trade organisations, trade union publications and professional organisations.

Musculoskeletal disorders

Musculoskeletal disorders include conditions affecting many parts of the body. They range from back injuries that may result from manual handling activities to upper limb disorders that may arise from repetitive movements, such as those involved in display screen equipment use.

Manual handling

Manual handling is all about moving. It includes physically lifting, lowering, holding, pushing, pulling, carrying or moving an object or load. Most manual handling accidents cause back injury, though hands, arms and feet are also vulnerable. Most manual handling injuries build up over a period of time rather than being caused by a single handling incident. These injuries can occur wherever people are at work - in hospitals, residential care homes, offices, shops or making deliveries - to name a few.

You, your employees and voluntary workers may be involved in all sorts of lifting and moving activities, from helping elderly people, to clearing rubbish, moving equipment, helping people with disabilities participate in sporting and recreational events, and even handling animals.

As manual handling causes so many injuries, there are specific regulations which set out ways to help you protect your employees. These are the Manual Handling Operations Regulations 1992. Duties under these Regulations do not extend to non-employees. However, the general duties under the HSW Act section 3 (see the section 'Legal duties') do require you to ensure their health and safety so far as is reasonably practicable. It would be good practice to extend the protective measures described in these Regulations to your voluntary workers.

The law requires you to avoid manual handling activities by employees which pose a risk of injury to them, so far as is reasonably practicable. If these activities can't be avoided, you must carry out a suitable and sufficient assessment of those activities and reduce any risks of injury to the lowest level reasonably practicable.

What do I need to think about?

You will probably have to think about a whole range of manual handling activities carried out during the course of your work. Some of them may be carried out away from your base work premises. Consider if the work involves:

- bending down;

- reaching up or down;

- stretching;

- twisting;

- stooping;

- repetitive movements;

- prolonged periods of activity;

- pushing or pulling;

- supporting static weights in one position.

Risk assessment for manual handling activities

Follow the *5 step* approach to risk assessment to find the precise risks and how to control them. Your significant findings should be recorded. Ask yourself if the activity is necessary - if not why do it? If the activity is necessary, you may be able to do away with some risks by redesigning work areas or work processes, or by introducing manual handling aids like hoists and pulleys.

Remember that you will need to carry out a new risk assessment if there are any significant changes to the work activities. Your risk assessment should take account of:

- the tasks;

- the individual performing the task;

- the load (inanimate or otherwise);

- the work environment.

The tasks

Do they include:

- holding loads away from the body;

- twisting, stooping or reaching upwards;

- large vertical movements;

- long carrying distances;

- strenuous pushing or pulling;

- unpredictable movement of loads;

- repetitive handling;

- insufficient rest or recovery time;

- a work rate imposed by process.

The individual performing the task

You may need to think about:

- *experience and training:* regular training is important in reinforcing correct procedures and for introducing new techniques and equipment;

- *strength:* some manual handling activities may require a certain level of strength;

- *stamina/level of fitness:* some risk activities occur regularly over prolonged periods and may require a certain level of stamina and fitness;

- *age:* you should not require a young person to do work that is beyond their physical capacity. Increasing age, too, may increase the risk of injury;

- *gender:* women generally do not have the same level of muscle development as men, although this does not automatically put them more at risk;

- *health status:* particularly any existing health or medical conditions. These may increase the risk of injury, eg backache, pregnancy, heart and/or breathing problems;

- *height:* this is particularly important in 'two person' lifts.

The load (inanimate or otherwise)

Inanimate

Common manual handling activities include moving furniture, delivering boxes of photocopying paper, pushing trolleys, removing and replacing heavy files and books from shelves.

Planning the storage of items on shelves so that heavy items are at chest height, and not below knee level or above shoulder level, can significantly reduce the risk of injury.

In charity shops, placing bags or trolleys for unwanted items next to the worker and in line with, and at the same height as, the sorting surface may eliminate the need for your worker to twist continually around and bend down.

Lifting or moving people, including children, and animals

Although you will approach manual handling activities which involve people or animals in the same way, there are particular problems you may need to take into account. For example, some people may refuse to be lifted by a hoist or become aggressive; certain medical conditions may cause your client to go into sudden fits and body spasms causing their bodies to become suddenly very rigid or very flexible.

Your clients should be encouraged to assist in any transfers or other manual handling activities as much as they are able to. In situations where a client is unable to do this, the use of transfer boards, turntables, standing belts, hoists, etc, should be used wherever possible to safeguard your worker and the dignity of the client. Your clients' care plans could include details of any agreed manual handling procedures such as hoisting, two person lifts, etc.

Remember to think about the risk of injury to your clients as well as to your employees.

Animals, of course, may do anything! They can be unpredictable or dangerous, or just simply unco-operative. Many lifts involving animals are also likely to be made from ground level and will almost certainly involve the animal struggling against their handlers.

You may need to think about:

- *weight:* train your employees to check the weight before committing themselves to a lift and to get help from colleagues;

- *physical size;*

- *flexibility or rigidity;*

- *shifting centre of gravity:* eg vessels containing fluids;

- *whether the load is made up of smaller units and whether these are securely bound together:* smaller or secure items are likely to be more easily moved or lifted, helping to reduce the risk to your workers.

The work environment

The environment, where the manual handling activity is carried out, is also important and may significantly increase the risk of injury. If your workers provide care in your client's own home, you have no legal right to require changes or the provision of equipment in order to control identified manual handling risks. However, you still have a duty to ensure, so far as is reasonable practicable, your workers' health and safety in such situations.

An initial assessment, with regular reviews, of the whole situation should identify the immediate problem areas, including necessary manual handling activities and aids. Where there are significant risks to a carer's health and safety which cannot be addressed, the service may need to be refused or withdrawn.

You may need to think about:

● *presence of other hazards:* hot, cold or slippery surfaces, sharp edges, splinters, etc;

● *presence or absence of secure handholds/grips;*

● *available space in which to carry out the activity:* spaces with restricted access may require people to bend while moving items if they cannot stand upright. Many old buildings, often used as administration centres, have small, steep and narrow stairways, particularly to higher floors. This may necessitate manually carrying up furniture and stationery items, etc; there is not always a lift access to these areas;

● *presence of any other factors such as obstructions;*

● *presence of available lifts.*

Upper limb disorders (ULDs)

ULDs are also called WRULDs (work-related upper limb disorders) and so-called, or commonly mistermed RSI (repetitive strain injuries). ULDs are conditions that can affect the neck, shoulders, arms, elbows, wrists, hands and fingers. They can occur in jobs that require: repetitive finger, hand, or arm movements; twisting movements; squeezing; hammering or pounding; or pushing, pulling, lifting or reaching movements.

You need to consider these risks as part of your risk assessments. If you do not act promptly, serious ill health could result.

Display screen equipment (DSE)

The use of display screen equipment such as personal computers has grown considerably in the last few years. If your employees (or self-employed people working at your undertaking) use DSE for a significant part of their working day, you need to arrange for their workstations to be assessed and for the workers to be properly trained in the use of the equipment.

Many people complain about upper limb disorders, backache, headaches and even stress from using their DSE, but a risk assessment will help reduce many of these problems. You need to consider the DSE itself and the worker using it, by advising on correct furniture and posture, the placement of the screen, keyboard and other equipment, planning frequent breaks, and the provision of eyesight tests and glasses, if needed. Remember to include workers who use laptops or other portable DSE as a significant part of their normal work.

Further advice is given in the HSE booklet *Working with VDUs*. This is available from HSE Books; an address is given at the end of this booklet.

Risk assessment for ULDs

Follow the *5 step* approach to risk assessment to find the precise risks and how to control them. Your significant findings should be recorded.

Work-related violence

(see also the sections 'Charity shops' and 'Working off-site ')

HSE defines work-related violence as: *any incident in which a person is abused, threatened or assaulted in circumstances relating to their work.*

Over the last few years, there has been a growing awareness of work-related violence and the effect this can have on people at work. The term *violence* brings to mind acts of physical harm, such as punching or kicking. In the workplace, violence is more often limited to verbal abuse, although the consequences to the victims may be no less traumatic. Employees and other workers who deal directly with the public may be sworn at, threatened or even attacked. Some of the latest figures indicate that approximately 1.4 million workers have been the victim of a physical assault.

Violence can result in physical harm but also in the psychological effects of either being assaulted or verbally threatened or abused. But some work-related violence is preventable, and the extent and severity of outcomes can be minimised.

The nature of some charity and voluntary work may put your employees and voluntary workers at risk from the violent or aggressive behaviour of others, including the general public. Remember that verbal abuse can be just as upsetting as a physical attack. Particular attention may need to be given to workers involved in the following activities.

Activities requiring particular attention

Providing a service

This could include many activities, such as meals-on-wheels or driving elderly people, and would bring your employees and voluntary workers into contact with many different clients.

Caring

Care-related work has the potential for violent situations to arise, particularly if your client, or their relatives, are reluctant to co-operate in the care programme.

There may be additional risks if the care is provided away from your work premises, in the client's home. Work with mentally ill people, or with people with learning disabilities or challenging behaviour, may also lead to violent situations. You need to think about how you would tell new workers about their new clients or how you would tell an existing client about necessary changes to their care plan.

Cash handling

Work involving the collecting and handling of money from fund-raising events, charity shops and other similar activities, offers the potential for another hazard - threat of theft or assault. Visiting private homes to raise funds can present potential dangers.

Charity shops

For more relevant details, you should see the section 'Charity shops'.

Reporting incidents of work-related violence

Assaults (acts of non-consensual physical violence) against an employee or self-employed person, which cause a major injury or result in someone being away from their normal work for more than three days, should be reported to your health and safety enforcing authority. Further details can be found in the section 'Reporting accidents and work-related ill health'.

What do I need to think about?

You should work together with your workers in identifying and addressing violent and potentially violent situations, in order to determine the scope of the problem. Identify which employees or voluntary workers are at risk; those who have face-to-face contact with the public are normally the most vulnerable. Where possible, you may try to identify potentially violent people in advance, perhaps a particularly difficult client that you provide care for, so that the risks from them can be minimised.

Check your existing arrangements, if you have them. Are the precautions in place adequate or should more be done? Remember it is usually a combination of factors that give rise to violence. But you can influence those factors. You may want to take action in the following areas:

- the level of training and information you and others can provide;

- the work environment;

- the design of the job.

The level of training and information you and others can provide

Your employees and other workers will need training to spot the early signs of aggression and to either avoid it or cope with it. You may focus your training on building good communication and social skills which play an important part in diffusing and preventing aggressive behaviour. You may find regular refresher training will help your workers remain competent and confident to deal with these situations. This does not need to be formal; a group session describing experiences can often deliver this.

You may also want to think about the specific needs of new employees or volunteers. They may be particularly vulnerable to work-related violence because of their inexperience.

Make sure your workers fully understand any system you have set up for their protection.

HSE has published guidance on violence at work that you may find useful. There are also other organisations that offer a variety of help and guidance on training techniques and methods. You will find some useful contacts and references at the end of this booklet.

The work environment

Consider the working environment as much as you can. If your workers have to visit people's homes, remember to make sure that someone knows where they are, when they can be expected back and what they can expect on arrival.

The design of the job

A good example of how you can effectively influence the design of the job or the work, is the handling of money from fund-raising events. It is unlikely that you will be able to control the amount of money, but you may want to think about:

- requesting cheques rather than cash where possible;

- ensuring cash boxes from stalls or attractions are not left out in the open; arrange for cash to be collected at various intervals (but be mindful of timed or regular collections);

- arranging for staff to be accompanied by a colleague if they have to take the money to the bank. If this is a regular activity, remember to vary the route taken and store the money in an inconspicuous bag or container;

- arranging for workers to be accompanied by a colleague if they have to meet an unknown contact at the person's home or at a remote location;

- arranging for workers who work away from your base to keep in touch. You may also want to think about how to avoid workers being alone or travelling home late at night.

You need to make sure that you have agreed and clearly understood procedures in place for dealing with violent attacks. Your workers need to be familiar with them so they know what to do if a problem occurs.

You may find it useful to record all acts, or near misses, of violence that your workers are exposed to. This may help you to identify trends that will help to target your control measures more effectively.

Your workers are likely to be committed to the measures you take if they help design them and put them into practice. A mix of measures often works best, particularly given the considerable range of activities you are likely to be involved in.

What about the victims?

If there is a violent incident involving your workers, you will need to respond quickly to avoid any long-term distress to employees. You may want to talk to your workers about the types of support that is available. Indeed, there are many charitable and volunteer organisations that offer support and help in this area: The Samaritans, Victim Support, etc. Contact details can be found at the end of this booklet.

Other employees and workers

As well as offering help and support to the primary victim of a violent incident, you should not forget that there may be secondary victims too; perhaps the incident was witnessed by a colleague. They may also experience traumatic symptoms.

You may want to think about the following areas of help.

Debriefing and counselling

Victims of work-related violence may have reactions to the incident. Symptoms such as an avoidance of situations that remind them of the incident, difficulty sleeping and flashbacks have all been recorded. Everyone is different and will cope with traumatic or upsetting experiences in different ways. But you may want to offer help and support.

Victims may want to talk through their experiences but counselling should not be imposed. Some employers use debriefing or diffusing counselling techniques to safeguard workers' mental well-being following incidents of violence at work. If you do decide to use these technique, you should have clear objectives and remember that it is important to evaluate them to make sure that they are meeting these objectives.

Time off or away from work

People react differently and are likely to take differing amounts of time to recover. Some people may prefer to return to work straight away. Be patient, and think about the available support mentioned above. It is important to keep in touch with people who are away from work, especially those who live on their own. But remember not to be intrusive.

Legal help

In serious cases legal help may be appropriate, particularly if there needs to be a decision about whether to prosecute the assailant.

Where can I go for advice?

You can ask your local environmental health department or HSE office for advice on the prevention and management of violence at work.

Work-related stress

Stress is people's natural reaction to excessive pressure - it isn't a disease. But if stress is excessive and goes on for some time, it can lead to mental and physical ill health (eg depression, nervous breakdown, heart disease).

It should be remembered though, that being under *pressure* often improves performance and can provide the drive for many of us to achieve. So, it can be a good thing. But when demands and pressures become excessive, they lead to stress.

You need to think about the nature of the work your employees and voluntary workers do. Some voluntary workers may withdraw their support if they are under stress for domestic reasons. But where they do work for you, voluntary workers should be offered the same consideration as their employed colleagues.

What do I need to think about?

Where the stress caused, or made worse, by work could lead to ill health, you must assess the risk in the same way that you would for the other areas covered in this booklet. You need to think about:

- pressures at work;

- deciding who might be harmed by these; and

- deciding whether you are doing enough to prevent harm.

So what causes stress?

All sorts of things are likely to create excessive and prolonged pressure. You're not under a legal duty to prevent ill health caused by stress due to problems outside work, eg financial or domestic. But non-work problems can make it difficult for people to cope with the pressures of work, and their performance might suffer. So try to be understanding to employees and voluntary workers in this position.

But what about at work? Some common causes of work-related stress include:

- too much work;

- too little work (boredom);

- confusing or conflicting demands;

- lack of recognition of work achievements;

- lack of control over the work;

- monotonous, repetitive work;

- poorly designed or inadequate workplaces;

- threat of violence or aggression, including bullying and harassment by managers or colleagues;

- providing care to others;

- work beyond or below the worker's capabilities.

What can I do about it?

There are lots of things you can do, depending on the nature of the work, how it is managed and what the specific issues are. But you may want to:

- change the way jobs are done, for example moving people between jobs, giving individuals more responsibility, increasing the scope of the job, increasing the variety of tasks or giving a group of workers greater responsibility for effective group performance;

- try to give warnings of urgent or important jobs;

- make sure individuals are matched to jobs;

- make sure everyone has defined tasks and responsibilities;

- provide training and support for those who care for others;

- provide training on interpersonal skills.

You might also want to think about providing or offering access to a counselling service. Although this doesn't always tackle the cause of stress, it can help people to cope with the consequences.

Remember these are just a few suggestions. You should talk to your workers to agree the best actions for you, them and the people you are helping.

What are the signs of stress?

The following list offers an indication of the types of physical and behavioural symptoms, but remember, people react to stress or excessive pressure in different ways.

behavioural	physical
increased anxiety	increased heart rate
increased irritability	sweating
aggression	headaches
insomnia	dizziness
changes in appearance or habits	blurred vision
poor concentration	aching neck and shoulders
increased sickness absence	skin rashes
isolation from work colleagues or deterioration in working relationships	
dependency on alcohol, tobacco or caffeine	
poor timekeeping	
inability to cope with routine or everyday tasks	

These symptoms are often short lived and can be reduced significantly when the cause of the stress has been tackled. If the cause is not addressed, the symptoms may become more serious and lead to longer term health problems. Your workers may display any one or all of these symptoms at any time. Quick recognition and remedial action are very important.

Reporting accidents and work-related ill health

The Reporting of Injuries, Diseases and Dangerous Occurrences Regulations 1995 (RIDDOR) require you to report some work-related accidents, diseases and dangerous occurrences. The Regulations apply to all work activities. If you are an employer, self-employed or in control of work premises you have duties under RIDDOR.

When do I need to make a report?

Death or major injury

If there is an accident arising out of or in connection with work and:

- your employee, or self-employed person working on your premises is killed or suffers a major injury* (including as a result of physical violence); or

- a member of the public is killed or taken to hospital;

you must notify the enforcing authority without delay (eg by telephone).

They will ask for brief details about your business, the injured person and the accident. Within ten days, you must follow this up with a completed accident report form (F2508), available from HSE Books (the address is given at the end of this booklet).

Over-three-day injury

If there is an accident arising out of or in connection with work (including an act of non-consensual physical violence) and your employee suffers an over-three-day injury, you must send a completed accident report form (F2508) to the enforcing authority within ten days. The same requirement applies if the accident happens to a self-employed person working on your premises.

---

* major injuries include fractures, amputations, loss of sight, unconsciousness, etc.

An over-three-day injury is one which is not major but results in the injured person either being unable to do the full range of their normal duties or being away from work for more than three days.

The three days include any days they wouldn't normally be expected to work such as weekends, rest days or holidays, but does *not* include the day of the injury itself.

Disease

If a doctor notifies you that your employee suffers from a reportable work-related disease, you must send a completed disease report from (F2508A) to the enforcing authority.

Dangerous occurrence

If something happens which does not result in a reportable injury, but which clearly could have done, then it may be a dangerous occurrence which must be reported immediately (eg by telephone) to the enforcing authority. Dangerous occurrences are listed in the Regulations and include: failure of lifts and hoists; collapse of scaffolding; fire or explosion which stops work for over 24 hours.

Within ten days you must follow this up with a completed accident report form (F2508). A form is included with this booklet which you may copy.

Who do I report to?

In general, you should contact the environmental health department of your local authority if your business is:

- office-based;

- retail or wholesale;

- warehousing;

- hotel and catering;

- sports or leisure;

- entertainment or other cultural or recreational activities, excluding broadcasting;

- residential accommodation, excluding nursing homes;

- concerned with places of worship;

- pre-school child care;

- mobile vending.

For all other types of business, it is the local area office of HSE. Look in the 'phone book under HSE to obtain the address and telephone number. If you have any difficulty obtaining the details, ring the HSE InfoLine (details at the end of the booklet).

What records do I need to keep?

You must keep a record of any reportable injury, disease or dangerous occurrence for three years from the date on which it occurred. This must include:

- the date and method of reporting;

- the date, time and place of the event;

- personal details of those involved; and

- a brief description of the nature of the event or disease.

You can keep the record in any form you wish.

Further details including report forms, lists of the major injuries, dangerous occurrences and diseases are available from HSE Books (see the references at the end of this booklet).

Accident investigation

Accident investigation is a useful tool to help you measure your health and safety performance standards. It can help to provide an effective means of communicating accident prevention lessons, as well as raising general health and safety awareness.

When should I investigate?

You may want to think about the following to help you decide which accidents you should investigate and to what degree:

- seriousness of consequences;

- actual loss;

- potential loss;

- numbers of people exposed;

- type of hazard;

- type of activity;

- likely recurrence of the accident;

- measures necessary to prevent a recurrence.

Your accident investigations should be methodical and determine the real cause, not the initially perceived cause.

Who should investigate an accident?

Your accident investigator should have your authority to ask questions, and should be able to gather and interpret information and evidence, both independently and by interviewing the people involved, or those who witnessed the accident.

Fire safety

Fire is a significant risk in many premises. Employers and providers of premises have to ensure the safety of those who work for them, and of those who use their premises. Their duties include the assessment of the fire risk. The risk assessment should cover:

- possible causes of fire;

- ways in which the risk of fire occurring and spreading, and the risk to people in case of fire, can be minimised;

- means of fighting fire;

- fire detection and warning;

- emergency routes and exits;

- information, instruction and training in fire precautions;

- maintenance and testing of fire precautions.

Detailed guidance on fire risk assessment will be published in Summer 1999 to accompany the Fire Precautions (Workplace) (Amendment) Regulations 1999. Advice will continue to be available from your local fire authority.

Legislation

Fire risks are covered by the Health and Safety at Work etc Act 1974 and the regulations made under it. In particular, the Management of Health and Safety at Work Regulations 1992 (as amended) require you to carry out an assessment of the fire risks. Enforcement responsibility for process fire precautions - that is, action to reduce the risk of outbreak or spread of fire - in charity and voluntary organisations, under health and safety legislation, usually lies with the local authority environmental health department.

There is, in addition, other legislation relating to general fire precautions, which is enforced by fire authorities and which are intended to protect people from the risk from fire. These include:

- The Fire Precautions Act 1971 - the Act works primarily through a fire certification procedure. Shops, offices, factories, railway premises and hotel type accommodation used by charity workers may need a fire certificate. Advice should be sought from your local fire authority;

- The Fire Precautions (Workplace) Regulations 1997 (to be amended by the Fire Precautions (Workplace) (Amendment) Regulations 1999).

Precautions

Action to ensure fire safety includes:

- *process fire precautions* - the special precautions in any premises in connection with the carrying on of any work process, including the use or storage of any article, material or substances in connection with or directly from that process, which are designed to prevent or reduce the likelihood of fire breaking out or its intensity; and

  general fire precautions - the means which are to be taken or observed in relation to the risk to the safety of employees in case of fire in a workplace, other than any special precautions in connection with the carrying on of any manufacturing process. They are the means of fire detection, warning, fire fighting and escape, ie ensuring that people can escape safely once a fire has started.

  The following paragraphs describe the types of process fire precautions and general fire precautions you should adopt in your organisation.

Process fire precautions

The main fire hazards are:

- handling/storage of flammable materials;

- poorly maintained, unsuitable or misused electrical equipment;

- smokers' materials;

- poor housekeeping/accumulation of waste material;

- arson.

Flammable materials can be found in most workplaces. They can range from textiles, clothing, packaging materials and plastic coat hangers to heating fuels and paint thinners. Many materials burn rapidly and produce dense smoke and toxic fumes (eg plastic foam, packaging, polyester wadding and textiles).

First, you should take measures to prevent fire starting and spreading. You can do this by controlling sources of ignition, and minimising the flammable materials available to fuel the fire:

- remove naked flames wherever possible (eg portable gas heaters) and ensure 'no smoking' rules are complied with;

- ensure you have the minimum amount of flammable materials necessary on the premises;

- store flammable materials safely and away from ignition sources;

- ensure good housekeeping to prevent the accumulation of flammable waste materials, and arrange regular collections of waste;

- use materials which are less flammable wherever possible, for example furnishings made of fire-resistant materials.

Highly flammable liquids

Small quantities of highly flammable liquids may be kept in a workroom (up to 50 litres) provided they are kept in a suitable fire-resisting cupboard or bin.

Liquefied petroleum gas (LPG) cylinders - butane and propane

The main risks from the use of LPG are:

- accidental release, which can lead to fire, explosion or asphyxiation;

- build-up of fumes or poisonous combustion products, particularly carbon monoxide.

Make sure that rooms where LPG powered appliances are used have sufficient high and low-level ventilation. The ventilation must never be blocked up to prevent drafts.

There are a number of precautions to take when storing and using LPG cylinders:

- store both full and empty cylinders in a secure well-ventilated position, away from other flammable materials and sources of ignition, preferably outside buildings;

- don't keep cylinders below ground level or next to drains, basements or other low-lying places;

- turn off cylinder valves before leaving the premises;

- change cylinders away from sources of ignition, in a well-ventilated place.

Tents and marquees

Tented, air-supported and pneumatic structures can present particular dangers. There are hazards of the ingitability of the material and rapid flame spread, together with the possibility of toxic smoke if plastics are present. Such structures need to be placed carefully, far enough apart to prevent fire spread and allow emergency access.

General fire precautions

If a fire does occur, the following measures need to be taken to prevent its spread:

- ensure fire-resistant doors, designed to stop the spread of fire and smoke, remain closed;

- provide enough extinguishers, of the right type and properly maintained, to deal promptly with small outbreaks of fire;

- where there is a risk of clothing catching fire, eg in kitchens, provide a suitable fire blanket;

- make sure staff know how to raise the alarm and how to use the extinguishers provided.

What to do in case of fire

When a fire occurs, the first priority must be to get everybody out safely. Protection of property is incidental. The person who first discovers the fire should raise the alarm, and the evacuation procedure for the workplace should be followed. You should only attempt to fight the fire if it is safe to do so.

However, you must take care because much of the danger from fire comes not from the actual flame but from heat and smoke, harmful gases, and lack of oxygen. If the premises must be evacuated, no-one should re-enter until the fire brigade say it is safe to do so.

The fire brigade should be summoned as soon as a fire is detected. It does not matter whether the fire has apparently been put out.

On leaving the premises, you should gather in a pre-arranged location. If you think anyone may still be inside, you should inform the fire brigade immediately.

Maintaining general fire precautions

All escape routes including passageways, corridors, and stairways should be checked regularly to make sure they are clear of obstruction and are available for use.

All fastenings on emergency exit doors should be checked to make sure they operate freely. Any defects should be repaired as soon as possible. All self-closing devices and automatic door holders/releases should be checked regularly to make sure they work properly.

All exit and directional signs should be checked to make sure they can be clearly seen at all times. All fire extinguishers should be checked regularly to confirm they are in position. They should be examined at least monthly to check they have not been discharged, lost pressure or suffered any obvious damage. Extinguishers should be tested and serviced annually by a competent person. Any used extinguisher should be serviced and replaced in its correct position as soon as possible.

Where hose reels are installed, they should be checked each month to confirm they are neither damaged or obstructed. They should be serviced annually by a competent person.

Where fitted, automatic sprinklers or other fixed fire-fighting equipment should be tested weekly (or in accordance with the installer's specifications) and serviced annually by a competent person.

Manually operated fire alarms should be checked to make sure they can still be heard throughout the workplace. Automatic and electrical warning systems should be tested weekly and serviced annually by a competent person.

A competent person should service automatic emergency escape lighting annually. It should be checked monthly to ensure it is in safe working order. Any portable lamps or torches should be tested weekly to ensure that they are available for use and operate efficiently.

If you would like more information about general fire safety, you should contact the fire safety office of your local fire authority (the telephone number for non-emergency calls is in the telephone book).

Health and safety enforcing authorities

Health and safety standards are enforced by HSE and by the environmental health departments of your local authority.

In general, you should contact the environmental health department of your local authority if your business or activities are:

- office-based;
- retail or wholesale;
- warehousing;
- hotel and catering;
- sports or leisure;
- entertainment or other cultural or recreational activities, excluding broadcasting;
- residential accommodation, excluding nursing homes;
- concerned with places of worship;
- pre-school child care;
- mobile vending.

For all other types of business it will be the local office of the HSE. Look in the 'phone book under HSE to obtain the address and telephone number. If you have any difficulty obtaining the details, ring the HSE InfoLine.

Health and safety regulations

Health and safety regulations that apply to all workplaces

Workplace (Health, Safety and Welfare) Regulations 1992 (SI 1992/3004)

Include requirements relating to the workplace, eg ventilation, heating, lighting, workstations, seating and welfare facilities.

Health and Safety (Display Screen Equipment) Regulations 1992 (SI 1992/2792)

Concern requirements for work with visual display units (VDUs).

Personal Protective Equipment at Work Regulations 1992 (SI 1992/2966)

Require employers to provide appropriate protective clothing and equipment for their employees where necessary.

Provision and Use of Work Equipment Regulations 1998 (PUWER) (SI 1998/2306)

Require that equipment provided for use at work, including machinery, is safe.

Manual Handling Operations Regulations 1992 (SI 1992/2793)

Cover the moving of objects by hand or bodily force.

Health and Safety (First Aid) Regulations 1981 (SI 1981/917)

Cover the requirements for first aid.

The Health and Safety Information for Employees Regulations 1989 (SI 1989/682)

Require employers to display a poster telling employees what they need to know about health and safety.

Employers' Liability (Compulsory Insurance) Regulations 1998 (SI 1998/2573)

Require employers to take out insurance against accidents and ill health to their employees.

Reporting of Injuries, Diseases and Dangerous Occurrences Regulations 1995 (RIDDOR) (SI 1995/2023)

Require employers to notify certain occupational injuries, diseases and dangerous events.

Noise at Work Regulations 1989 (SI 1989/1790)

Require employers to take action to protect employees from hearing damage.

Electricity at Work Regulations 1989 (SI 1989/635)

Require people in control of electrical systems to ensure they are safe to use and maintained in a safe condition.

Control of Substances Hazardous to Health Regulations 1999 (COSHH) (SI 1999/437)

Require employers to assess the risks from hazardous substances and take appropriate precautions.

In addition, specific regulations cover particular areas, for example asbestos and lead, and:

Construction (Design and Management) Regulations 1994 (SI 1994/3140 as amended SI 1996/1592)

Cover safe systems of work on construction sites.

Gas Safety (Installation and Use) Regulations 1998 (SI 1998/2451)

Cover safe installation, maintenance and use of gas systems and appliances in domestic and commercial premises.

The Health and Safety (Young Persons) Regulations 1997 (SI 1997/135)

Set out the requirements for the protection of young people at work.

Useful HSE publications

This list is not exhaustive but offers a sample of the guidance available from HSE. If you require guidance on a specific health and safety issue not mentioned here, or you would like to know more about an issue, you should call your local environmental health department or HSE's InfoLine (see Useful contacts) for advice.

Please note that where 'free leaflet' is indicated, there may be a charge for multiple copies.

Legal duties

A guide to the Health and Safety at Work etc Act 1974 L1 1992 ISBN 0 7176 0441 1

Health and safety regulations: a short guide HSC13 1995 (free leaflet)

Successful health and safety management HSG65 1997 ISBN 0 7176 1276 7

Management of health and safety at work. Management of Health and Safety at Work Regulations 1992. Approved Code of Practice L21 1992 ISBN 0 7176 0412 8

Young people at work: a guide for employers HSG165 1997 ISBN 0 7176 1285 6

New and expectant mothers at work: a guide for employers HSG122 1994 ISBN 0 7176 0826 3

Risk assessment

Managing health and safety: five steps to success INDG275 1998 (free leaflet)

Five steps to risk assessment INDG163 1998 (free leaflet)

A step by step guide to COSHH assessment HSG97 1993 ISBN 0 11 886379 7

COSHH: a brief guide to the Regulations INDG136(rev1) 1999 (free leaflet)

Manual handling: solutions you can handle HSG115 1994 ISBN 0 7176 0693 7

Information, instruction and training

5 steps to information, instruction and training INDG213 1996 (free leaflet)

Fund-raising

Entertainment and leisure

Fairground and amusement parks EIS5 1997 (free leaflet)

Managing crowds safely HSG154 1996 ISBN 0 7176 1180 9

Managing crowds safely INDG142 1993 (free leaflet)

Fireworks

Giving your own firework display: how to run and fire it safely HSG124 1995
ISBN 0 7176 0836 0

First aid

First aid at work: your questions answered INDG214 1997 ISBN 0 7176 1074 8

Working off-site

Working alone in safety INDG73(rev) 1998 (free leaflet)

Working with equipment

Safe use of work equipment. Provision and Use of Work Equipment Regulations 1998.
Approved Code of Practice and guidance L22 1998 ISBN 0 7176 1626 6

Personal protective equipment at work. Personal Protective Equipment at Work
Regulations 1992. Guidance on Regulations L25 1992 ISBN 0 7176 0415 2

Electricity at work: safe working practices HSG85 1993 ISBN 0 7176 0442 X

Maintaining portable and transportable electrical equipment HSG107 1994
ISBN 0 7176 0715 1

Musculoskeletal disorders

Work related upper limb disorders: a guide to prevention HSG160 1990

ISBN 0 7176 0475 6

Manual handling. Manual Handling Regulations 1992. Guidance on Regulations L23

1998 ISBN 0 7176 0411 X

Manual handling: solutions you can handle HSG115 1994 ISBN 0 7176 0693 7

A pain in your workplace? Ergonomic problems and solutions HSG121 1994

ISBN 0 7176 0668 6

Working with VDUs INDG36(rev1) 1998 ISBN 0 7176 1504 9 (free leaflet)

VDUs: an easy guide to the regulations. How to comply with the Health and

Safety (Display Screen Equipment) Regulations 1992 HSG90 1994 ISBN 0 7176 0735 6

Work-related violence

Violence at work: a guide for employers INDG69(rev) 1997 (free leaflet)

Preventing violence to retail staff HSG133 1995 ISBN 0 7176 0891 3

Violence and aggression to staff in the health services: guidance on assessment

and management 1997 ISBN 0 7176 1466 2

Violence in the education sector 1997 ISBN 0 7176 1293 7

Work-related stress

Stress at work: a guide for employers HSG116 1995 ISBN 0 7176 0733 X

Help on work-related stress: a short guide INDG281 1998 (free leaflet)

Reporting accidents and work-related ill health

RIDDOR explained HSE31(rev1) 1999 ISBN 0 7176 2441 2 (free leaflet)

A guide to the Reporting of Injuries, Diseases and Dangerous Occurrences

Regulations 1995 L73 1999 ISBN 0 7176 2431 5

Report of an injury, dangerous occurrence or case of disease RIDDOR 1995 Forms

F2508 and F2508A ISBN 0 7176 1114 0

Video

Charity and voluntary organisations: a health and safety video exercise. A video accompanies this booklet, priced £25. Order forms are available from:

Local Authority Unit

HSE

7th floor, South Wing

Rose Court, 2 Southwark Bridge

London SE1 9HS

Tel: 0171 717 6686

While every effort has been made to ensure the accuracy of the references listed in this publication, their future availability cannot be guaranteed.

Useful contacts

Details of how to obtain publications from HSE Books are given at the end of the booklet.

For enquiries about health and safety, ring HSE's InfoLine Tel: 0541 545500, or write to HSE's Information Centre, Broad Lane, Sheffield S3 7HQ

HSE home page on the World Wide Web:
http://www.open.gov.uk/hse/hsehome.htm

Your local library may have access to the Internet.

Other useful contacts

Charities Safety Group
PO Box 804, Croydon CR9 8BJ
Tel: 0700 900 9128

Victim Support:

In England: **Victim Support**
National Office, Cranmer House
39 Brixton Road, London SW9 6DZ
Tel: 0171 735 9166

In Scotland: **Victim Support Scotland**
14 Frederick Street, Edinburgh
Tel: 0131 225 8233

The Samaritans
You can find contact details for your local Samaritans office in the 'phone book.

Crime prevention officers

You can find contact details for your local crime prevention officer in the 'phone book.

Fire brigades

Further information regarding fire safety is obtainable from: the Fire Policy Unit, Home Office, Horseferry House, Dean Ryle Street, London SW1P 2AW

Tel: 0171 217 8734

Gas safety

The use of LPG cylinders in mobile catering vehicles and similar commercial vehicles. Available from:

The LP Gas Association, Alma House, Alma Road, Reigate, Surrey, RH2 0AZ

Printed and published by the Health and Safety Executive

C50   05/99

Health and Safety at Work etc Act 1974
The Reporting of Injuries, Diseases and Dangerous Occurrences Regulations 1995

Report of an injury or dangerous occurrence

Filling in this form
This form must be filled in by an employer or other responsible person.

Part A

About you

1 What is your full name?

2 What is your job title?

3 What is your telephone number?

About your organisation

4 What is the name of your organisation?

5 What is its address and postcode?

6 What type of work does the organisation do?

Part B

About the incident

1 On what date did the incident happen?

/ /

2 At what time did the incident happen?
(Please use the 24-hour clock eg 0600)

3 Did the incident happen at the above address?

Yes ☐ Go to question 4

No ☐ Where did the incident happen?

☐ elsewhere in your organisation – give the name, address and postcode
☐ at someone else's premises – give the name, address and postcode
☐ in a public place – give details of where it happened

If you do not know the postcode, what is the name of the local authority?

4 In which department, or where on the premises, did the incident happen?

Part C

About the injured person

If you are reporting a dangerous occurrence, go to Part F.
If more than one person was injured in the same incident, please attach the details asked for in Part C and Part D for each injured person.

1 What is their full name?

2 What is their home address and postcode?

3 What is their home phone number?

4 How old are they?

5 Are they

☐ male?
☐ female?

6 What is their job title?

7 Was the injured person (tick only one box)

☐ one of your employees?
☐ on a training scheme? Give details:

☐ on work experience?
☐ employed by someone else? Give details of the employer:

☐ self-employed and at work?
☐ a member of the public?

Part D

About the injury

1 What was the injury? (eg fracture, laceration)

2 What part of the body was injured?

3 Was the injury (tick the one box that applies)

☐ a fatality?

☐ a major injury or condition? (see accompanying notes)

☐ an injury to an employee or self-employed person which prevented them doing their normal work for more than 3 days?

☐ an injury to a member of the public which meant they had to be taken from the scene of the accident to a hospital for treatment?

4 Did the injured person (tick all the boxes that apply)

☐ become unconscious?

☐ need resuscitation?

☐ remain in hospital for more than 24 hours?

☐ none of the above.

Part E

About the kind of accident

Please tick the one box that best describes what happened, then go to Part G.

☐ Contact with moving machinery or material being machined

☐ Hit by a moving, flying or falling object

☐ Hit by a moving vehicle

☐ Hit something fixed or stationary

☐ Injured while handling, lifting or carrying

☐ Slipped, tripped or fell on the same level

☐ Fell from a height

How high was the fall?

[   ] metres

☐ Trapped by something collapsing

☐ Drowned or asphyxiated

☐ Exposed to, or in contact with, a harmful substance

☐ Exposed to fire

☐ Exposed to an explosion

☐ Contact with electricity or an electrical discharge

☐ Injured by an animal

☐ Physically assaulted by a person

☐ Another kind of accident (describe it in Part G)

Part F

Dangerous occurrences

Enter the number of the dangerous occurrence you are reporting. (The numbers are given in the Regulations and in the notes which accompany this form)

[   ]

Part G

Describing what happened

Give as much detail as you can. For instance
- the name of any substance involved
- the name and type of any machine involved
- the events that led to the incident
- the part played by any people.

If it was a personal injury, give details of what the person was doing. Describe any action that has since been taken to prevent a similar incident. Use a separate piece of paper if you need to.

☐☐☐☐ [   ]

Part H

Your signature

Signature

[   ]

Date

[/   /   ]

Where to send the form

Please send it to the Enforcing Authority for the place where it happened. If you do not know the Enforcing Authority, send it to the nearest HSE office.

For official use

Client number

[   ]

Location number

[   ]

Event number

[   ]

☐ INV   REP ☐ Y ☐